Because We All
Stayed Home...

Because We All Stayed Home...

Written by
ELIZABETH GOLDMAN

Illustrated by
SOME VERY SPECIAL PEOPLE

Illustrations by the children in my 2020 and 2021 classes and my family.

Thank you to the children whose illustrations brought my words to life.

Thank you to Karolina Wudniak for formatting my book and advising me throughout the process.

First paperback edition, September 2021

Library of Congress Control Number
ISBN 978-1-7369779-1-0 (paperback)
ISBN 978-1-7369779-0-3 (ebook)

Cover and interior design by Karolina Wudniak
www.karolinawudniak.com

This book is dedicated to my own personal heroes:

My family with whom I spent a lot of time in quarantine! Brian, Abby, Grace, Jake and Reen. I love you beyond words.

My students of 2020. Your little faces made everything better.

My parents who are no longer with me, but continue to inspire me everyday.

Eileen and Don who always believed in me.

To the frontline workers who sacrificed so much for so many.

Things will get better. It has already begun.

William Ponce

We all stayed home.
There was nothing we could do.

We all stayed home,
For this wasn't just the flu.

Madison Granados

We all stayed home
And spent time with family.

We all stayed home
Until we began to see,

Yannis Tam

The helpers come from everywhere,
To do their jobs each day.

While families huddled in their homes,
And we began to pray.

Ella Troche

That there would be a way out soon,
And then the kids would cheer!

"Back to school we go!"
"Let's get out of here!"

Abigail Goldman

Masks and gloves protected us,

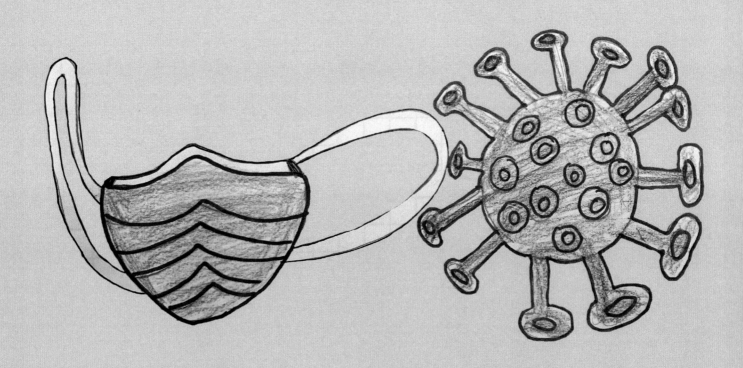

Jayden Lee

While scientists worked hard,

Bianca Rodrigues DeOliveira

Dominic Ortiz

Children made get well cards.

Lediona Kabashi

Kids and parents worked from home
Trying hard to make their way,

Through all the things they had to do
Each and everyday.

Caio DeSouza

But in the meantime, silver linings shone
And lit up darkened clouds.

Maeve Reilly

The sirens rang at 7 pm.
And they were mighty loud!

Jayden Lee

The clapping for our healthcare teams
Would sound throughout our blocks.

Firefighters and police crews
came about in flocks!

Ryan Flaherty

Jackson DeCillis

To honor all the helpers,
From the frontlines to the back

From saving people's lives
To handing out the snacks.

Yannis Tam

People came together
From near and very far.

Jacob Goldman

Special occasions were celebrated
In parades, with lines of cars.

Maya Abrahmov

Some of us had tough times,
When things just all seemed wrong.

Then virtual choirs got online
And sang for us a song.

Maureen Collins

A song of hope, a song of love
A song of peace and light

To celebrate what we believe
That things would soon be right.

Grace Goldman

And then one day
The sun came up

And things began to change.

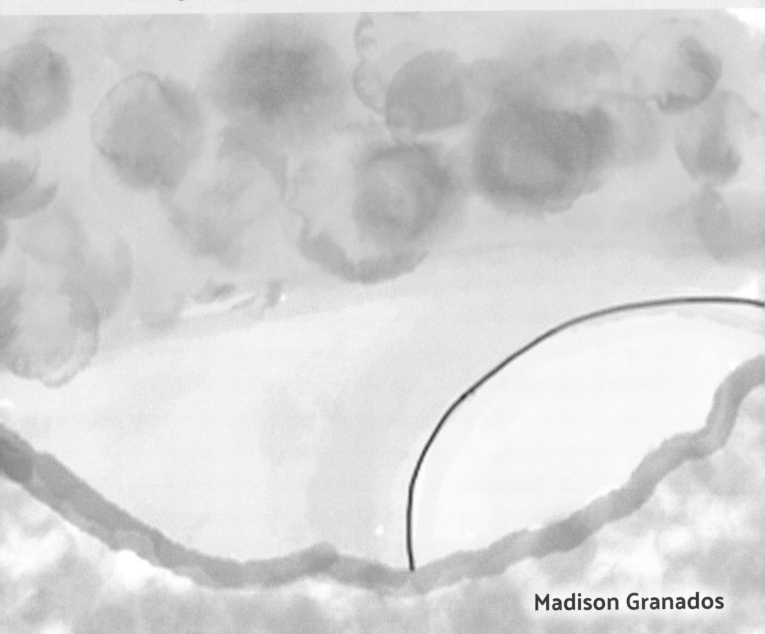

Madison Granados

Slowly, steadily folks got well.
The leaders said, "Ok!"

"The people CAN go back to work!"
"Come on kids, go and play!"

Bianca Rodrigues DeOliveira

We've learned our lessons.
We'll be smart,

No matter where we roam.
We'll ease back in, and grow from here,

Jaxon Gandarela

Because we all stayed home!

Emma Schettino

Made in the USA
Middletown, DE
02 October 2021